Smart Phonics 2

e-future

Smart Phonics 2 Contents

Constant and Cumulative Review

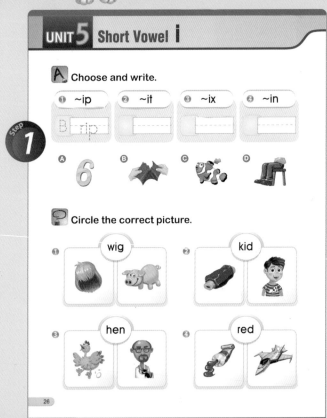

UNIT 5 Short Vowel i

step **1**

A. Choose and write.

① ~ip	② ~it	③ ~ix	④ ~in

B rip

A 6   B   C   D

Circle the correct picture.

① wig

② kid

③ hen

④ red

26

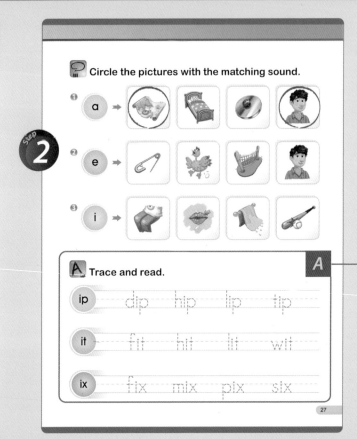

Circle the pictures with the matching sound.

① a →

② e →

③ i →

step **2**

A. Trace and read.

ip	dip	hip	lip	tip
it	fit	hit	lit	wit
ix	fix	mix	pix	six

A

27

Smart Phonics 2

Step	Cumulative Target Practice	Skills
1	New Targets	Reading/Writing
2	New & Old Targets 1	Reading/Writing + Reading Extension (A)
3	New & Old Targets 2	Reading/Writing
4	New & Old Targets 3	Reading/Writing + Visualization (B)
5	New Targets	Writing

is Key to Success in Learning Phonics!

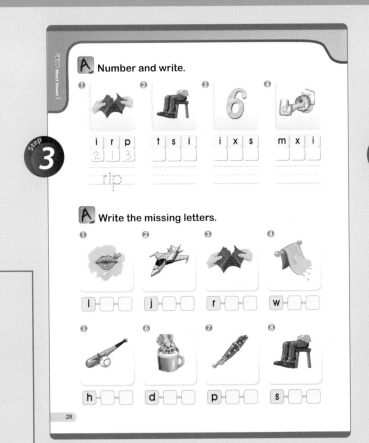

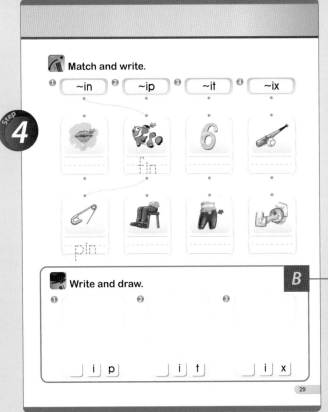

Challenge Your Brain!

A Reading Extension

Children use their newly acquired phonics skills to read selected words that are not introduced in the student book. This activity will prepare children for reading outside of phonics class.

B Visualization

Children choose words with the target sounds, visualize the pictures of the words and draw them in the space provided. This activity will help children remember the target words and sounds better.

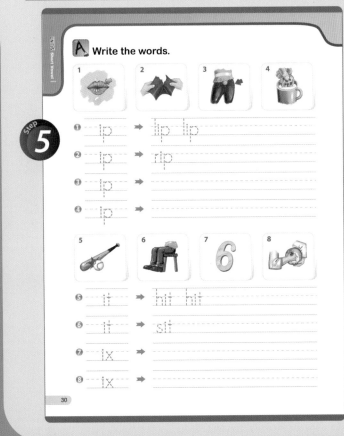

Circle and write.

①

(h)
g
→ h + am → ham

②
r
l
→ ___ + am → ___

③
b
d
→ ___ + am → ___

④
c
k
→ ___ + ap → ___

⑤
r
l
→ ___ + ap → ___

⑥
m
n
→ ___ + ap → ___

Number and write.

①

a	j	m
2	1	3

jam

②

n	p	a

③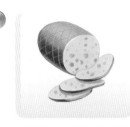

a	m	h

④

c	p	a

⑤

m	r	a

⑥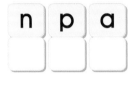

m	p	a

⑦

m	d	a

⑧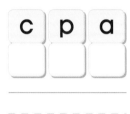

l	p	a

 Trace and read.

am   dam   Pam   ram   Sam

ap   cap   gap   lap   tap

Match and write.

① ~am

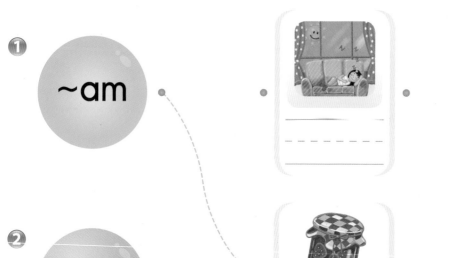

jam

② ~ap

 Write the missing letters.

①

c a p

②

h ☐ ☐

③

m ☐ ☐

④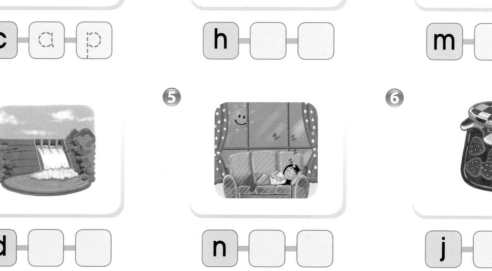

d ☐ ☐

⑤ n ☐ ☐

⑥ j ☐ ☐

Choose and write.

① ~am

A ham	

② ~ap

A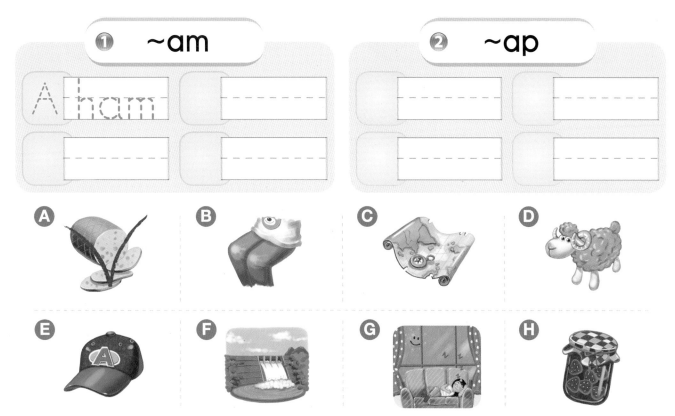
B
C
D

E
F
G
H

 Write and draw.

① ② ③

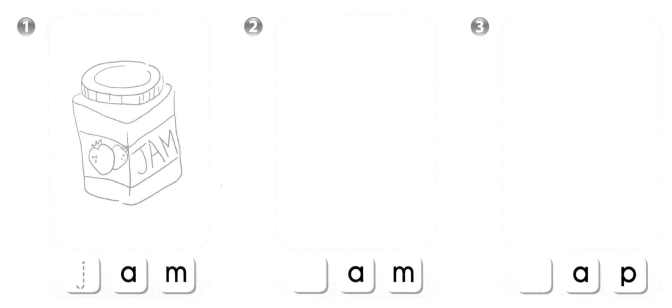

j a m   a m   a p

Write the words.

① am ➡ ham ham

② am ➡ dam

③ am ➡

④ am ➡

⑤ ap ➡ cap cap

⑥ ap ➡

⑦ ap ➡

⑧ ap ➡

Circle and write.

①

(c)
k
→ c + an → can

②

f
p
→ ___ + an → ___

③

n
m
→ ___ + an → ___

④

b
d
→ ___ + at → ___

⑤

s
c
→ ___ + at → ___

⑥

k
h
→ ___ + at → ___

Circle the correct word.

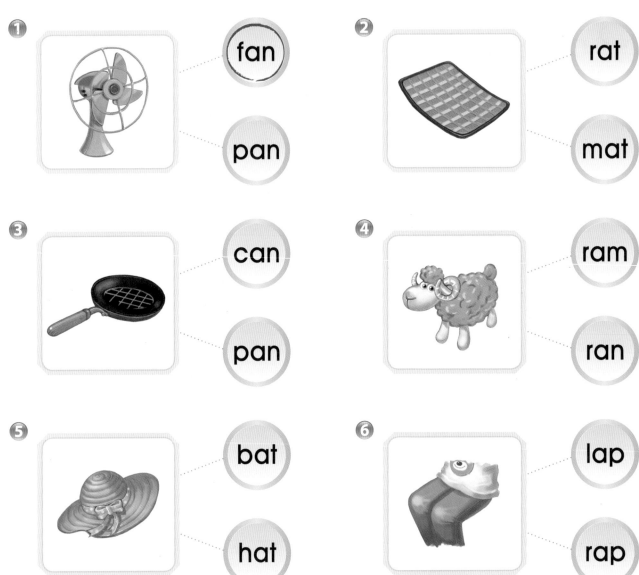

① fan
pan

② rat
mat

③ can
pan

④ ram
ran

⑤ bat
hat

⑥ lap
rap

 Trace and read.

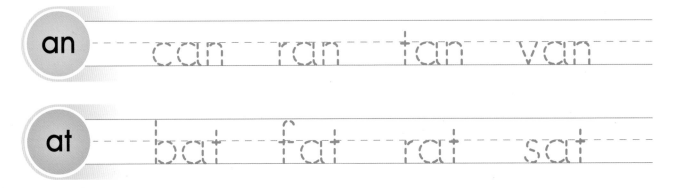

an   can ran tan van

at   bat fat rat sat

Circle the correct picture.

1. can
2. bat
3. fan
4. cat
5. man
6. hat
7. pan
8. mat

Find and circle.

①

p w b **(a** b **a t** r

②

b n **c a n** z x y u

③

w **m a n** r e x n m

④

k l w z q u **m a t**

⑤

l u s w **p a n** y t

⑥

c b **m a p** w e r a

 Write and draw.

①

c | a | n

②

| a | n

③

| a | t

Write the words.

1  **2**  **3**  **4**

1. an ➡ can can
2. an ➡ fan
3. an ➡
4. an ➡

5  **6**  **7**  **8**

5. at ➡ bat bat
6. at ➡ cat
7. at ➡
8. at ➡

Circle and write.

①

(b) d → b + ed → bed

②

l r → ___ + ed → ___

③

k h → ___ + en → ___

④

p b → ___ + en → ___

⑤

y j → ___ + et → ___

⑥

w v → ___ + et → ___

Choose and write.

① ~ed
② ~en
③ ~et

B bed

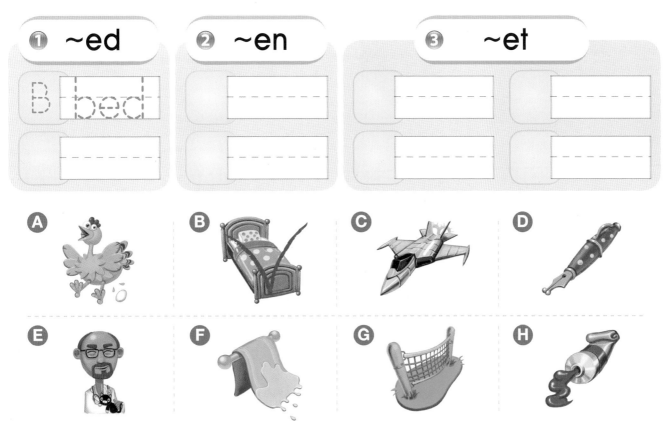

Ⓐ Ⓑ Ⓒ Ⓓ
Ⓔ Ⓕ Ⓖ Ⓗ

 Circle the correct picture.

① nap
② pen
③ jam
④ wet

Find and circle.

①

②

③

④

| opqram⃝l | jgrcaph | mzcanwf | xhatmye |

⑤

⑥

⑦

⑧

| ikredrx | zhxuvet | henqkis | cponetx |

 Trace and read.

ed
bed fed led red

en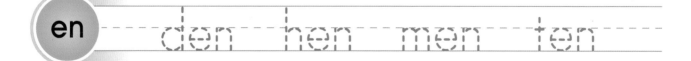
den hen men ten

et
get jet vet wet

Write the missing letters.

①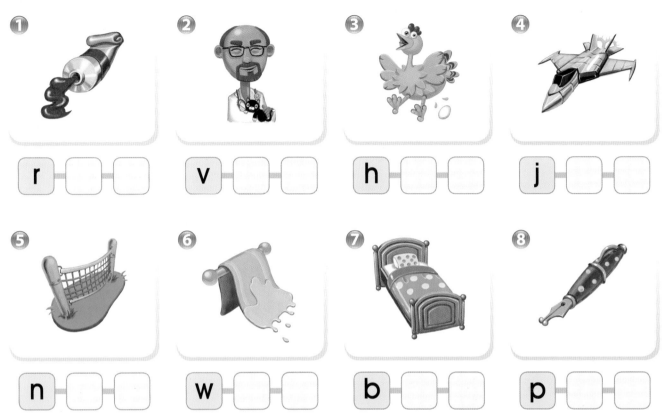
r ⬜ ⬜

②
v ⬜ ⬜

③
h ⬜ ⬜

④
j ⬜ ⬜

⑤
n ⬜ ⬜

⑥
w ⬜ ⬜

⑦
b ⬜ ⬜

⑧
p ⬜ ⬜

 Write and draw.

①
⬜ e d

②
⬜ e n

③
⬜ e t

Write the words.

① _ed_ ➡ bed bed

② _ed_ ➡ red

③ _en_ ➡

④ _en_ ➡

⑤ _et_ ➡ wet wet

⑥ _et_ ➡ vet

⑦ _et_ ➡

⑧ _et_ ➡

 UNIT 3 Short Vowel e

 20

Write the missing letters.

① r ☐ ☐

② f ☐ ☐

③ l ☐ ☐

④ b ☐ ☐

⑤ p ☐ ☐

⑥ k ☐ ☐

⑦ w ☐ ☐

⑧ p ☐ ☐

 Trace and read.

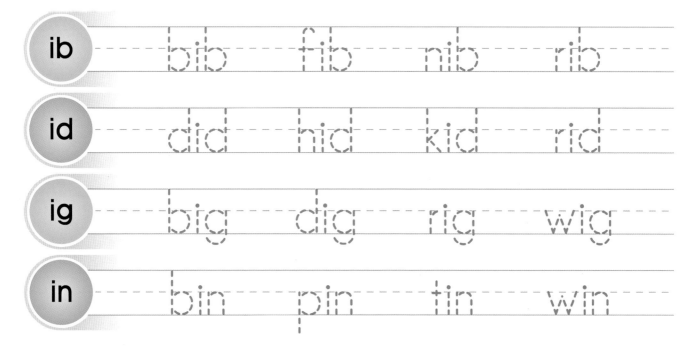

ib	bib	fib	nib	rib
id	did	hid	kid	rid
ig	big	dig	rig	wig
in	bin	pin	tin	win

Circle the correct word.

1.

bib

rib

2.

pen

hen

3.

net

jet

4.

pig

wig

5.

lid

kid

6.

pin

fin

 Find and circle.

1.   2.   3.   4.

w d r i b k a   w k i d p m z   x y w i g u b   c s c z p i n

Match and write.

~ib	~id	~ig	~in

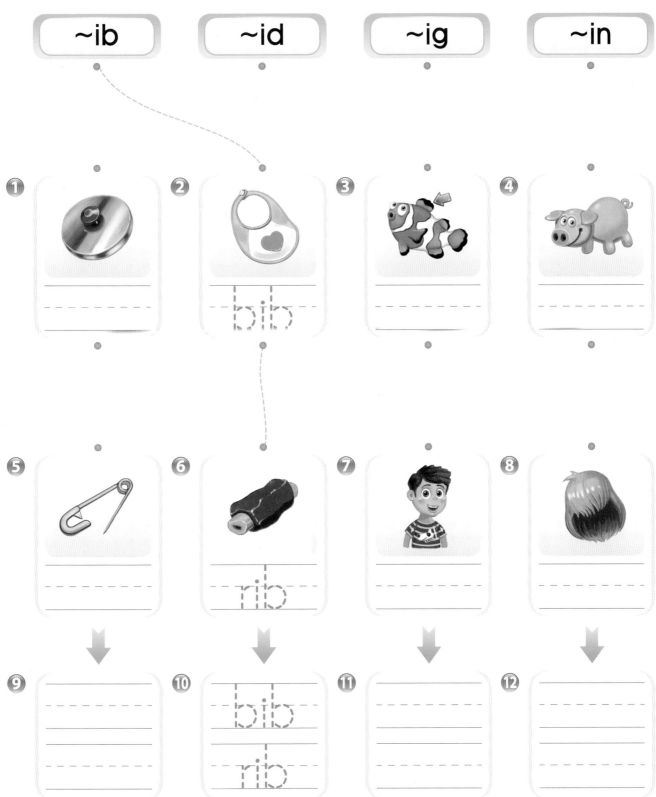

① _____

② bib

③ _____

④ _____

⑤ _____

⑥ rib

⑦ _____

⑧ _____

⑨ _____

⑩ bib
rib

⑪ _____

⑫ _____

Circle the correct picture.

① lid

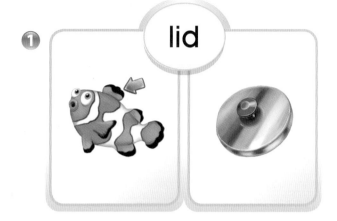

② bed

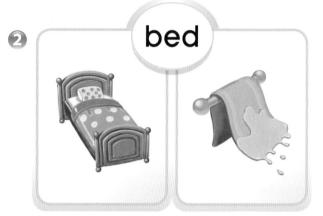

③ pig

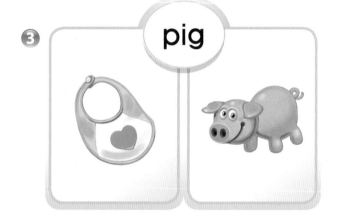

④ pen

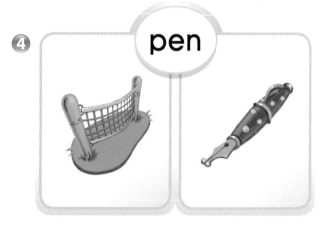

 Write and draw.

① ② ③ ④

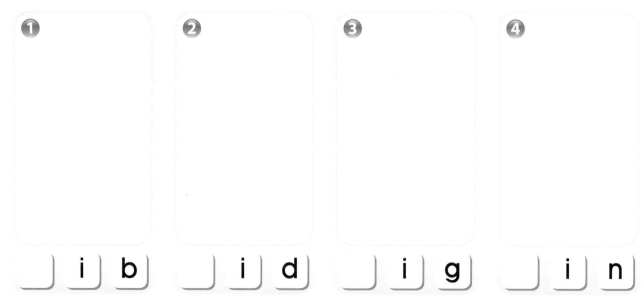

| i | b | | i | d | | i | g | | i | n |

Write the words.

1	2	3	4

1. ⬤ ib ➡ bib bib

2. ⬤ ib ➡ rib

3. ⬤ id ➡

4. ⬤ id ➡

5	6	7	8

5. ⬤ ig ➡ pig pig

6. ⬤ ig ➡ wig

7. ⬤ in ➡

8. ⬤ in ➡

Choose and write.

❶ ~ip	❷ ~it	❸ ~ix	❹ ~in
B rip			

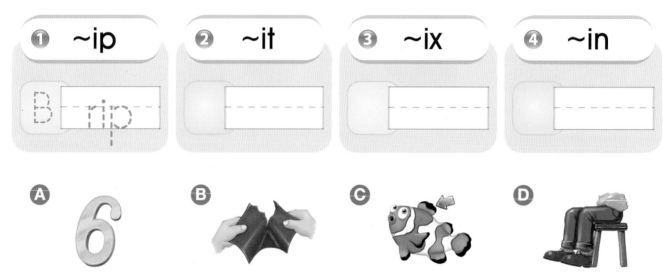

Ⓐ Ⓑ Ⓒ Ⓓ

 Circle the correct picture.

❶ **wig**

❷ **kid**

❸ **hen**

❹ **red**

Circle the pictures with the matching sound.

① a →

② e →

③ i →

 Trace and read.

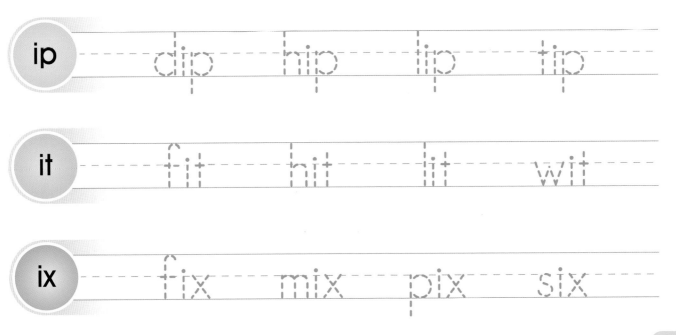

ip   dip   hip   lip   tip

it   fit   hit   lit   wit

ix   fix   mix   pix   six

A Number and write.

①

i	r	p
2	1	3

rip

②

t	s	i

③

i	x	s

④

m	x	i

A Write the missing letters.

①

l □ □

②

j □ □

③

r □ □

④

w □ □

⑤

h □ □

⑥

d □ □

⑦

p □ □

⑧

s □ □

Match and write.

1 ~in   **2** ~ip   **3** ~it   **4** ~ix

fin

pin

 Write and draw.

1 i p   **2** i t   **3** i x

Write the words.

1  **2**  **3**  **4**

① ip → lip lip

② ip → rip

③ ip →

④ ip →

5 **6** **7**   **8**

⑤ it → hit hit

⑥ it → sit

⑦ ix →

⑧ ix →

Match.

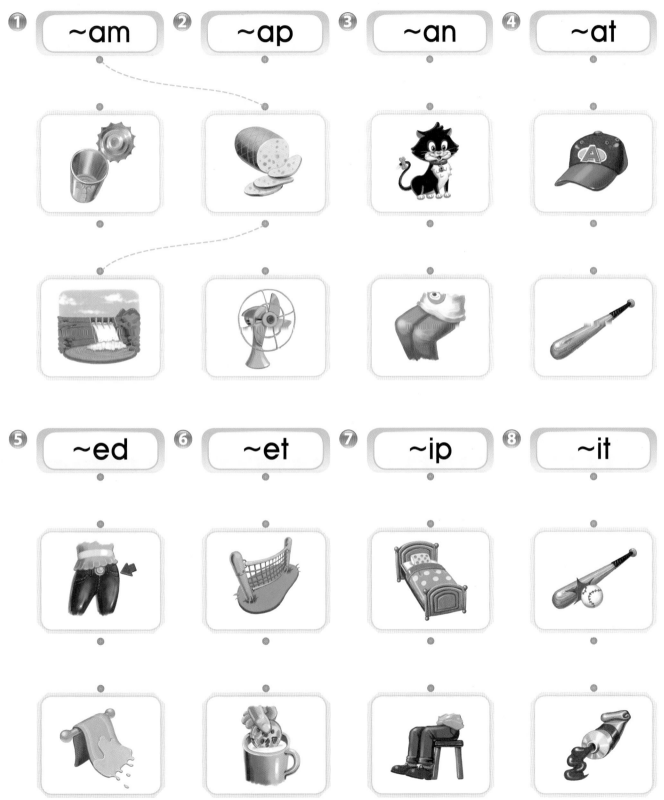

1. ~am
2. ~ap
3. ~an
4. ~at

5. ~ed
6. ~et
7. ~ip
8. ~it

Write the words.

①

kid kid

②

③

④

⑤

⑥

Circle the pictures with the matching sound.

① a →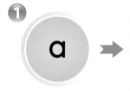

② e →

③ i →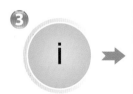

Circle and write.

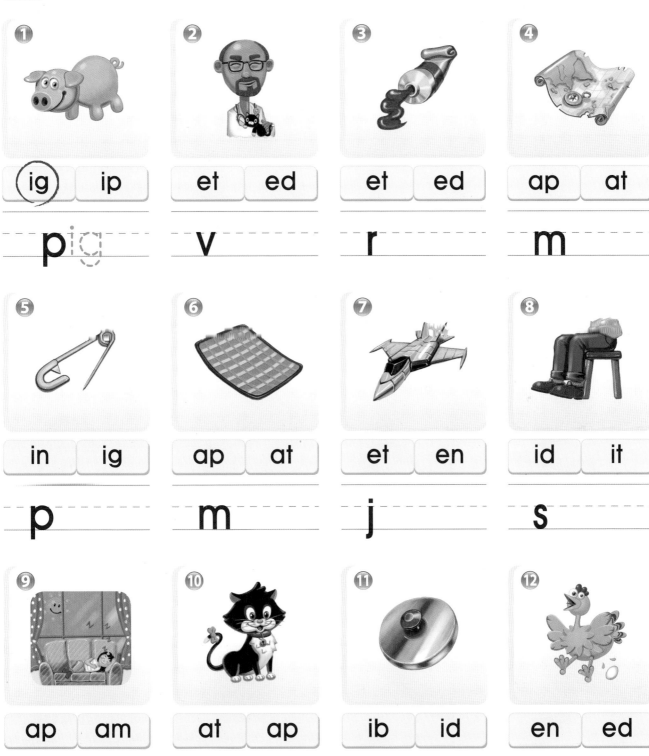

1. (ig)   ip
    p **ig**

2. et   ed
    v

3. et   ed
    r

4. ap   at
    m

5. in   ig
    p

6. ap   at
    m

7. et   en
    j

8. id   it
    s

9. ap   am
    n

10. at   ap
    c

11. ib   id
    l

12. en   ed
    h

Write the missing letter.

①

r [i] p

②

n [ ] t

③

h [ ] m

④

r [ ] b

⑤

d [ ] m

⑥

p [ ] n

⑦

c [ ] n

⑧

s [ ] x

⑨

j [ ] t

⑩

m [ ] x

⑪

h [ ] n

⑫

k [ ] d

⑬

v [ ] t

⑭

b [ ] t

⑮

w [ ] g

⑯

w [ ] t

Do the puzzle.

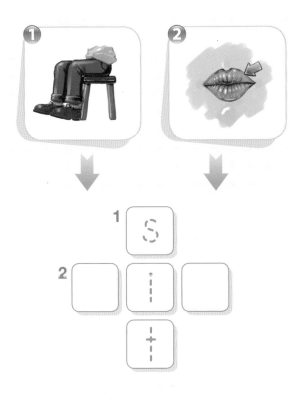

1 S
2 [ ] i [ ]
   t

3 [ ]
4 [ ] [ ] [ ]
   [ ]

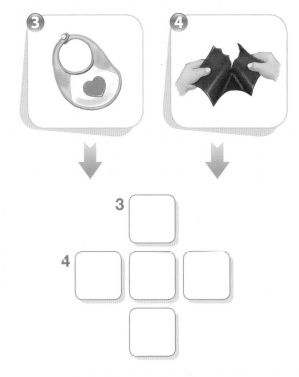

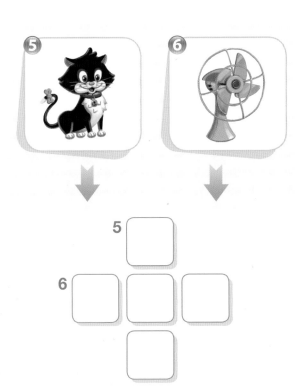

5 [ ]
6 [ ] [ ] [ ]
   [ ]

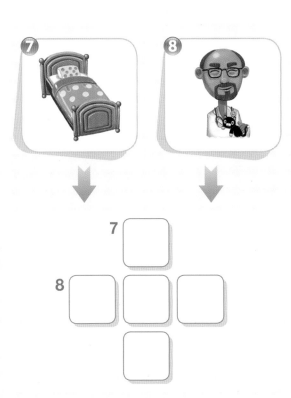

7 [ ]
8 [ ] [ ] [ ]
   [ ]

Choose and write.

❶ ~og	❷ ~op	❸ ~ot	❹ ~ox
B dog			

Ⓐ Ⓑ Ⓒ Ⓓ

 Trace and read.

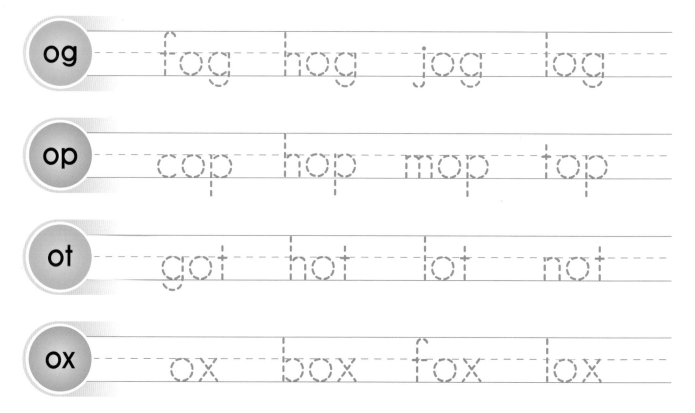

og — fog hog jog log

op — cop hop mop top

ot — got hot lot not

ox — ox box fox lox

Find and circle.

① wlxlogq **②** ejcopyu **③** hotnosg **④** swfoxqy

 Circle the picture with the same ending sound.

① A  B  C

②  A  B  C

③  A  B  C

④  A  B  C

A Write the words.

①

dog dog

②

③

④

⑤

⑥

⑦

⑧

⑨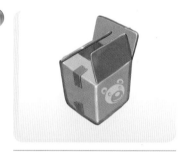

⑩

⑪

⑫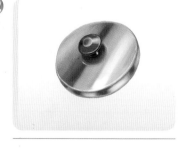

Write the missing letters.

① c ☐ ☐

② p ☐ ☐

③ d ☐ ☐

④ h ☐ ☐

⑤ b ☐ ☐

⑥ l ☐ ☐

⑦ h ☐ ☐

⑧ f ☐ ☐

 Write and draw.

① ☐ o g

② ☐ o p

③ ☐ o t

④ ☐ o x

Write the words.

1  **2**  **3**  **4**

① og ➜ dog dog

② og ➜ log

③ op ➜

④ op ➜

5  **6**  **7**  **8**

⑤ ot ➜ pot pot

⑥ ot ➜ hot

⑦ ox ➜

⑧ ox ➜

40

Circle the correct word.

1
- bug
- log

2
- rug
- log

3
- pot
- cup

4
- hug
- hit

5
- top
- tub

6
- pup
- fox

 Trace and read.

ub	hub	pub	rub	sub
ug	dug	hug	mug	tug
up	up	cup	pup	sup

Match and write.

1. e

2. i

3. o

4. u

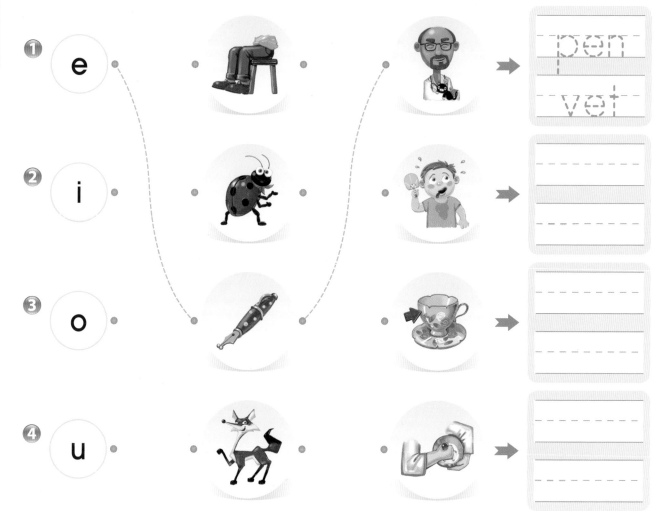

pen

vet

 Circle the pictures with the matching sound.

1. u →

2. o →

Circle the correct picture.

① mug

② pup

③ bug

④ rub

⑤ hug

⑥ cup

⑦ tub

⑧ rug

Write the missing letters.

 ①

s

 ②

b

③

d

④

l

⑤

h

⑥

c

⑦

p

⑧

h

 Write and draw.

① ② ③

u b

u g

u p

Write the words.

1

2

3

4

① ub ➡ rub rub

② ub ➡ tub

③ up ➡

④ up ➡

5

6

7

8

⑤ ug ➡ bug bug

⑥ ug ➡ hug

⑦ ug ➡

⑧ ug ➡

Match and write.

| ~ug | ~ud | ~un | ~ut |

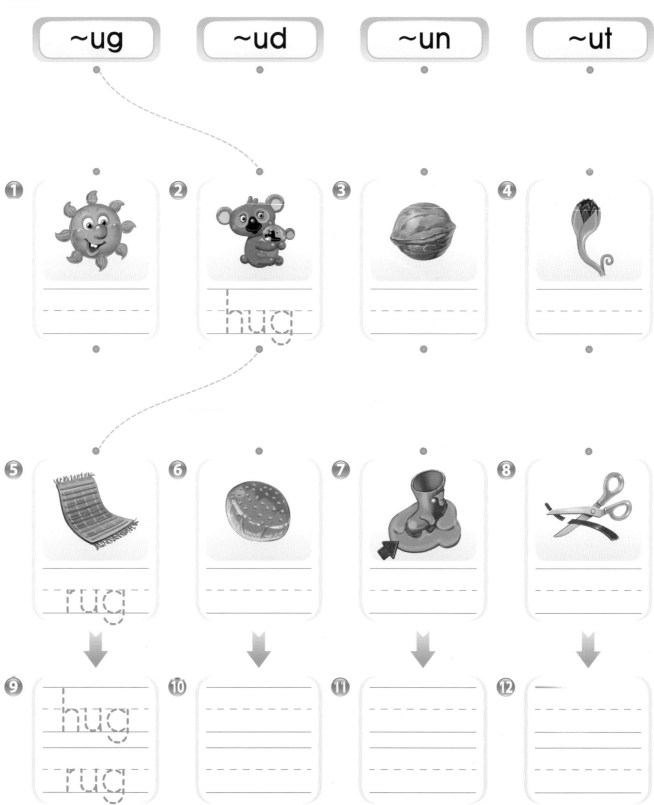

①

② hug

③

④

⑤ rug

⑥

⑦

⑧

⑨ hug rug

⑩

⑪

⑫

Find and circle.

①

wlxru**nq**

②

yh**op**nuo

③

b**ug**tgsw

④

kt**ub**gqy

⑤

slz**mud**f

⑥

gunzelx

⑦

os**pcop**s

⑧

w**cut**qys

 Trace and read.

ud	bud cud mud sud
un	fun nun run sun
ut	but cut hut nut

Do the puzzle.

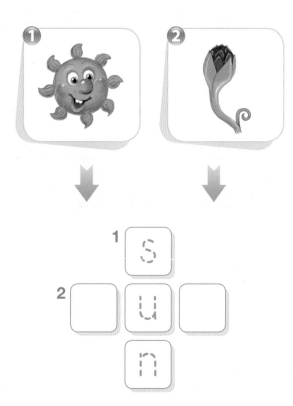

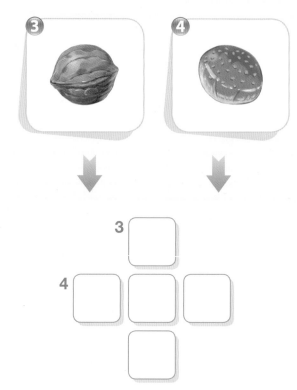

1 | s |

2 | | u | |

| n |

3 | |

4 | | | |

| |

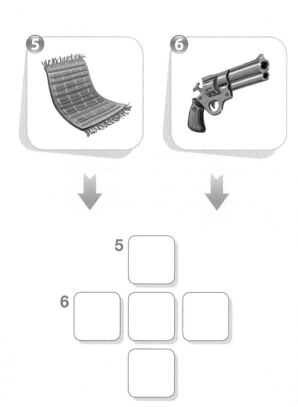

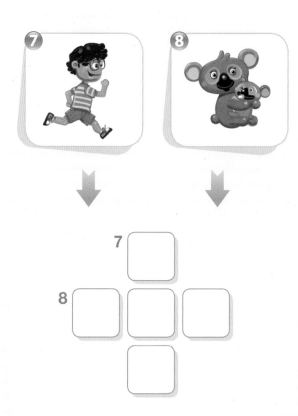

5 | |

6 | | | |

| |

7 | |

8 | | | |

| |

Write the words.

①

pup pup

②

③

④

⑤

⑥

 Write and draw.

①

u d

②

u n

③

u t

Write the words.

1. un ➡ sun sun
2. un ➡ bun
3. un ➡
4. un ➡

5. ud ➡ bud bud
6. ud ➡ mud
7. ut ➡
8. ut ➡

Number and write.

1

u s n

2 1 3

sun

2

g d o

_____

3

u t n

_____

4

u p p

_____

5

d m u

_____

6

f x o

_____

7

g b u

_____

8

l g o

_____

Circle the pictures with the matching sound.

① o →

② u →

 Circle the correct letters.

①
b   og   ot   (ox)

②
h   ug   up   un

③
c   og   op   ox

④
c   up   un   ut

⑤
d   og   ox   ot

⑥
r   un   ut   ug

Do the puzzle.

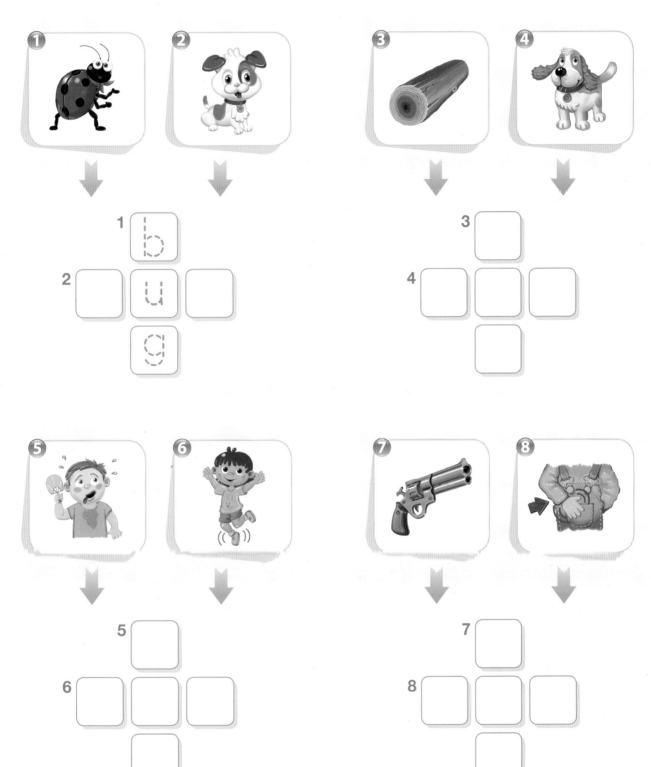

Write the missing letter.

1.

h **u** g

2.

b __ n

3.

c __ p

4.

t __ b

5.

g __ n

6.

l __ g

7.

c __ p

8.

n __ t

9.

d __ g

10.

r __ b

11.

b __ x

12.

r __ n

13.

c __ t

14.

h __ t

15.

r __ g

16.

p __ t

Match and write.

① ② ③ ④

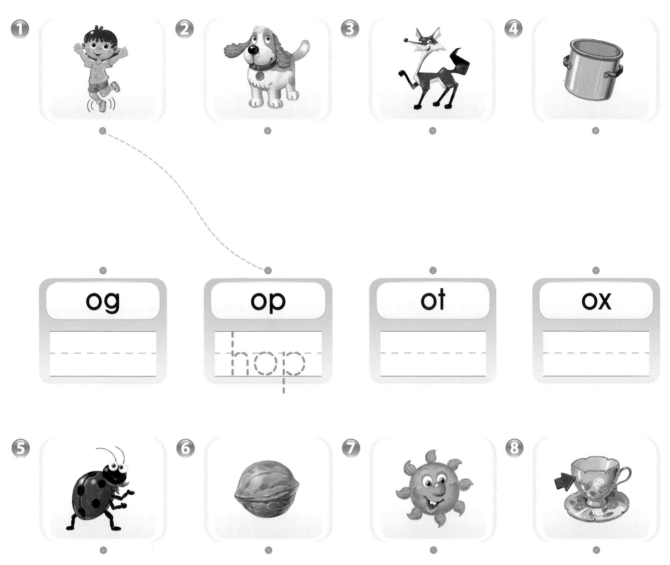

og	op	ot	ox
	hop		

⑤ ⑥ ⑦ ⑧

un	up	ug	ut

Write the missing letters.

①

p ☐ ☐

②

k ☐ ☐

③

h ☐ ☐

④

d ☐ ☐

⑤

w ☐ ☐

⑥

b ☐ ☐

⑦

f ☐ ☐

⑧

r ☐ ☐

⑨

m ☐ ☐

⑩

l ☐ ☐

⑪

b ☐ ☐

⑫

b ☐ ☐

⑬

h ☐ ☐

⑭

r ☐ ☐

⑮

h ☐ ☐

⑯

c ☐ ☐

Write the words.

①

red red

②

③

④

⑤

⑥

⑦

⑧

⑨

⑩

⑪

⑫

Circle the correct word.

1  dam / jam

2  pin / fin

3  pig / wig

4  map / lap

5  fin / fan

6  vet / wet

7  pen / pan

8  rub / tub

9  rug / mug

10  hot / hop

11  six / mix

12  nut / cut

Find and circle.

① w   (m   a   n)   y   p   c

② a   g   h   e   u   p   l

③ h   a   t   s   g   q   e

④ b   n   c   r   a   m   u

⑤ o   s   h   e   n   r   t

⑥ d   o   g   i   t   e   x

⑦ w   p   k   j   p   o   t

⑧ x   n   e   t   v   c   n

⑨ r   t   y   l   i   d   m

⑩ z   a   h   o   t   l   k

1	2	3	4	5

6	7	8	9	10

Smart
Phonics